THREE   DIMENSIONAL
PROJECTION DRAWING

THREE DIMENSIONAL PROJECTION DRAWING

By

P. J. BOOKER, Grad. I.E.D.

with a Foreword by

W. E. WALTERS, F.I.E.D.

President of the Institution of Engineering Draughtsmen and Designers

MODEL & ALLIED PUBLICATIONS
Argus Books Ltd.
14 St James Road,
Watford, Herts.

© Argus Books Ltd 1977

Revised and Reprinted December, 1954
Revised and Reprinted 1960 to conform with B.S. 308A
Reprinted December 1968

This edition 1977

Printed in Great Britain by Unwin Brothers Limited,
The Gresham Press Old Woking Surrey England
for Model & Allied Publications, Argus Books Ltd.
14 St James Road, Watford, Herts

Produced by offset lithography

FOREWORD

VISUAL shape-description by means of three-dimensional projection drawings is a subject of far-reaching importance to all who are engaged on the initial manufacture of engineering products and machinery. The need for such drawings has never been denied by any progressive engineer. However, to realise the need is not the same as to satisfy it.

The possible means of preparing pictorial views range from artistic talent to mechanical devices including entire draughting machines.

Engineering draughtsmen do not appear to take readily to such aids. They are accustomed to deal with the problems of drawing by applying conventional methods of projection. It is therefore to be expected that the advantages of three-dimensional drawings would be available to industry on a much larger scale if their preparation were in line with existing drawing office practice.

In developing the projection system which forms the subject matter of this book, I endeavoured to solve the problems of shape-description in such a manner that the work conforms with standard D.O. practice and can be carried out with no more than the ordinary instruments.

It is, perhaps, a sign of appreciation and recognition that the author should have chosen to base his book on the results of my research. Whether his preference for my projection method is indicative of its comparative merit is a question which the reader will be interested to decide for himself—and having decided, his views should be made known.

The system rests solidly on the rules of orthographic projection and makes use of the standard isometric angle of view, thereby providing a background which is familiar to all engineering draughtsmen and technical students. By marrying the fundamentals of orthographic and isometric drawing, a new technique was evolved which allows a component to be depicted in any aspect that may be required to produce the most informative view. The drawing procedure reduces mental visualisation to a minimum and is, incidentally, one of the most effective means of checking the accuracy of the orthographic original.

There are many other advantages which result from the use of three-dimensional drawings. The following—although incomplete—will help to direct some attention to the beneficial consequences :—

Manufacturers can utilise " green " labour with greatly increased efficiency ;

Workers can be trusted to read the drawings correctly and rapidly;

Shop executives can devote their time exclusively to their proper duties, instead of settling " blueprint queries ";

Production engineers can plan the operations with almost final certainty;

And—perhaps most important—the designer himself has an opportunity of physically seeing the result of his thought *before* production commences and when the inevitable modifications can be made most economically.

I have pleasure in recommending this book for study and congratulate the author not only on his own complete mastery of the subject, but also on his success in presenting it in text and illustrations which the reader cannot fail to follow with interest and understanding.

London, 1949   W. E. WALTERS.

I

A CENTURY or more ago, when mechanical devices were comparatively rare, the designer and the manufacturer were more often than not, one and the same person. The methods were mainly trial and error, but in those days they usually served their purpose.

Today, however, the growth of industry has necessitated the building up of great organisations in which production is divided into stages. The designer now restricts himself to design, using experience and mathematics to formulate his plans. His ideas are then conveyed to all those concerned in the further stages of the manufacturing process. Part of the information about a design can be put into words and figures, such as finish, dimensions, and material, but one very important factor, namely that of shape, can only be shown adequately through the medium of graphic delineation.

It is conventional in the engineering world to use orthographic projection for this shape description, a technique which shows plan, side and front elevations assuming three directions of view each at right angles to the others. The drawings of Fig. 1 are of this type.

As man-made articles are planned, they usually assume regular shapes, machined faces being automatically made square with one another unless there is a specific reason why they should not be so designed.

The lines of sight for these orthographic views, therefore, usually fall normal to surfaces, which is of great advantage in so far as the latter are then shown in their true shape. However, it is only the true shape of the *individual faces* which is shown, not—and this is specially noteworthy—the actual shape of the *whole solid item*. Orthographic views show only areas instead of space and solidity. Thus it is left to the imagination of the craftsmen, and others who have to read the drawing, to build up a true picture of the component in their own minds. It is here that errors in interpretation can and do arise, particularly where both first and third angle projection are in use. Even when the craftsman is fully experienced and, therefore, competent in his trade, much time is inevitably lost in

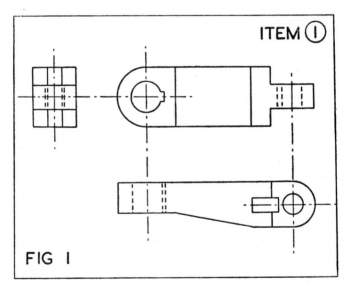

mentally welding together the three or more separate views. Fig. 1 contains only a simple item, but in spite of its simplicity, the true shape does not automatically spring to mind—it has to be " figured out."

Unlike an artistic effort, a machine drawing must not allow each viewer the scope of interpreting it as he sees fit. It must be an exact formula which should be read and applied accurately without any doubt as to its message. Orthographic views—necessary as they are for dimensioning—fall short in regard to shape description in that they leave the final step of complete interpretation to minds other than those of the designers.

The most efficient way to eliminate this failing is to present, together with the orthographic views, a pictorial one showing the real space relationship between the faces of the component to be made.

Professor William Farish realised this need nearly 150 years ago when he introduced the isometric drawing technique which has since been used by a number of draughtsmen to implement and clarify the presentation of their ideas. The isometric system does produce pictorial views, but owing to its inherent limitations it cannot always show the illustrated item to the best advantage. This is sometimes a greater drawback than it would seem at first, as important details may be entirely invisible. Apart from this there is the problem of constructing the pictorial circle, which is, of course, the ellipse.

Many schemes have been devised to produce pictorial views by mechanical means with the object of allowing greater scope in the choice of a viewpoint, and greater facility in dealing with curved outlines,

3

but they have never been of much practical use because the amount of work entailed was always out of all proportion to the results achieved. The real cause for this failure lay in the fact that orthographic and pictorial projection were divorced from each other. This forced the draughtsman to go through the same mental process of unreliable visualisation which he was trying to save the craftsman. Although the problems of three-dimensional shape description by *direct projection* are by no means easy to solve, a new method is now available which affords a *practicable* means of translating orthographic plans and elevations without prior visualisation. This workable system, first published in *Engineering Drawing and Design* was developed by W. E. Walters, the founder of the Institution of Engineering Draughtsmen and Designers.

In addition to the standard drawing equipment, no other apparatus is required, and this, with the advantages of mechanical simplicity, makes the system quite acceptable for normal drawing office use. The object of this book is to present briefly, but adequately, the essentials of the Walters system by means of building up three-dimensional views in easy stages.

I I

In building up a three-dimensional view of a component, the only information concerning its shape is vested in its orthographic outlines, and it, therefore, follows that these views must be used as the basis throughout.

A simple geometrical solid, the cube, will serve to demonstrate the problem which must be solved. The top diagram of Fig. 2 shows a cube as seen along the line of the arrow normal to a face, which, of course gives one of the orthographic views, that is, a plain square. This by itself is obviously inadequate to depict a solid form. There is no " depth " in it. It might represent a surface—not necessarily a vertical one—or the face of a prism with any number of details hidden from sight. In brief, it is ambiguous and lacks *definition of shape.*

Rotating or tilting the cube, as in the next two stages of Fig. 2, brings one other face into view. In the first case the *front* and a *side* can be seen, while in the second one the *top* and *front* are in sight. Such outlines are still not fully informative because they give no indication as to how far the faces extend in space, neither is there any information to show what— if anything—lies behind them.

It is evident, then, that only a view showing *three faces* will clearly describe shape, and this can be accomplished only by applying both *rotation and tilt* to the

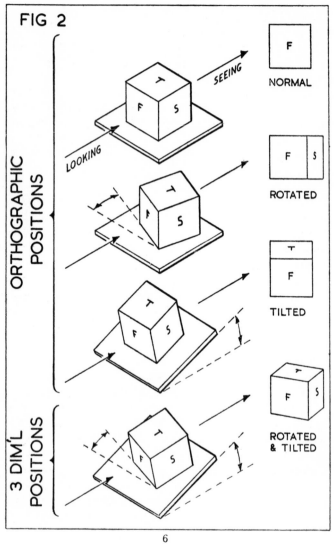

FIG 2

ORTHOGRAPHIC POSITIONS

3 DIM'L POSITIONS

SEEING

LOOKING

NORMAL

ROTATED

TILTED

ROTATED & TILTED

object. The result is illustrated in the last stage of
Fig. 2. The problem is now clear. It is to find a
reasonable method of drawing " three face views "
from the original scale projections with as few inter-
mediate steps as possible.

When any line is turned out of the normal position
it appears to shorten, so that in the three-face-view of
the cube none of the edges can be drawn true length.
It must also be noted that the degree of foreshortening
is not the same for all lines. In addition the angles
between the edges also distort and may appear greater
or lesser than their true value.

It is, of course, easy to project rotated *or* tilted views,
but the problem is more complex when rotation *and*
tilt are applied together. However, even this problem
may be solved by normal projection in two stages.

This two-stage method is shown in Fig. 3, and is no
doubt familiar to most draughtsmen. The views
A, B and C at the top of this figure are the normal
orthographic outlines of a cube, while beneath these
the elevations D and E, in the first stage, are those
of the original plan rotated, F. In the second stage,
the side elevation is tilted, G, and from this and the
rotated plan, F, the final three-dimensional view H
is projected. In this final sequence, the plan used, F,
is *not* the true plan of the cube in this three-dimensional
view, for it is a view along the line of the arrow Q,
and not along that of P. The plan F may be used
for this last projection, however, because the lengths b,
c and d are parallel with the axis of tilt and, therefore,
do not change in length. This principle, namely
that lengths in, or parallel with, the axis of tilt (or rotation) do not change, is very important and is the basis

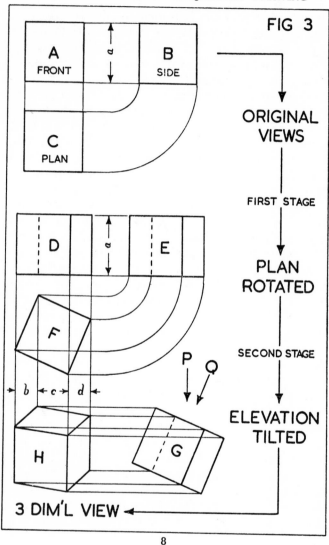

FIG 3

A
FRONT

B
SIDE

a

C
PLAN

ORIGINAL
VIEWS

FIRST STAGE

D   E

a

PLAN
ROTATED

F

SECOND STAGE

P Q

b   c   d

ELEVATION
TILTED

H   G

3 DIM'L VIEW ◄

of all projection techniques. It was used automatically —perhaps unnoticed—when the cube was rotated in the first stage of Fig. 3, and the height of the rotated elevations was naturally made the same as that in the normal views (dimension *a*).

Of the two orthographic outlines, F and G, used for projecting this three-dimensional view, H, one, the rotated plan F, is exactly the same as the original C, except for its relative position. The other, the rotated and tilted side elevation G, is entirely different from the original, B, and has had to be specially drawn to carry out the three dimensional construction, H. This makes the two-stage method uneconomical in space, time and effort, especially when the object is complicated, as a practical example is bound to be.

If the construction of this special side elevation, G, which is not needed in itself, could be dispensed with completely, the method would begin to assume a form suitable for practical use. Although it may not appear feasible at first sight, the Walters system has made this possible, and the next chapter will show in stages how it is done.

I I I

ONE of the simplest of shapes is a square. It can quickly be drawn in any position, but even more so at 45 deg. rotation, as shown in Fig. 4(A), when the plan may be constructed with a 45 deg. set square. Its elevation then becomes a line equal in length to its diagonal. This square will be referred to from now on as the *basic square*.

The tilted view of this square is obviously a rhombus, Fig. 4(B), which can be projected from the plan in (A) and the tilted elevation in (B) in the same way as the three dimensional view in Fig. 3 was developed. The major diagonal, *a*, remains true length, while the " tilted " length of the minor one, *b*, is foreshortened.

Now, any point on the perimeter of the plan square in (A), must also lie on the perimeter of the view in (B), and as lengths parallel with the axis of tilt do not change, such points must lie projectionally in line. It follows that the correct point on the rhombus corresponding to a point on the square is found readily by simply dropping a projector as in normal orthographic drawing.

If a square at any chosen angle of rotation is superimposed upon the basic square (Fig. 4(C)) they intersect in eight points—shown ringed—all of which may be projected directly on to the rhombus. The eight points in C lie in the outlines of the superimposed

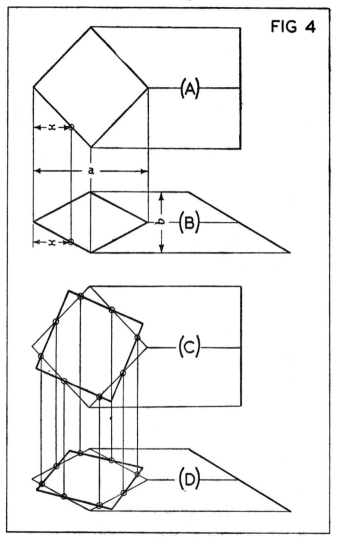

FIG 4

(A)

(B)

(C)

(D)

square, so that the corresponding points on the rhombus in (D) must lie in the three dimensional outlines of the chosen square. Therefore, it is necessary only to draw the appropriate lines through the intersections on the rhombus and the result is the correct translation of the superimposed square.

If this had been the top face of a cube, the other faces would have to be drawn as in Fig. 5. The simplest way to do this is to complete first the *basic cube*, which is the cube whose plan is the basic square. To draw the three dimensional view of this basic cube, the foreshortened height is all that need be found. This height can be projected in the same way as the minor diagonal of the rhombus in Fig. 4(B), and is shown projected in Fig. 5. When the basic cube is completed, its top and base appear as identical rhombuses, so that the points of intersection in the plan may be immediately projected on to *both* rhombuses. In this way the three dimensional view of the top and bottom faces are determined, and it is necessary only to join the corners of the one face to those of the other with vertical lines to complete the picture.

These last lines are obviously all the same length as each is tilted to the same degree. In practice, therefore, it is unnecessary to construct the lower rhombus and complete the basic cube, because the vertical edges may be stepped off with the appropriate length along the projectors dropped from the corners of the three dimensional top face.

The method, so far developed, still entails the construction of an auxiliary view, X, although the essential part of this view consists only of the two

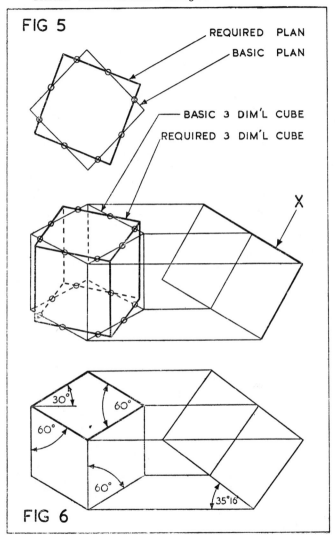

FIG 5

REQUIRED PLAN
BASIC PLAN

BASIC 3 DIM'L CUBE
REQUIRED 3 DIM'L CUBE

X

30°
60°
60°
60°
35°16'

FIG 6

heavy lines, which are far easier to draw than the complex view used originally in Fig. 3.

However, this can be reduced still further, but only by introducing a limitation—a standard angle of tilt. The resulting restriction is justifiable because it reduces the amount of work and simplifies the whole procedure; furthermore, as will be seen, the limitation is not so great as it at first appears.

If a suitable angle of tilt is chosen as a standard, the rhombus can be made to assume a shape in which all its sides slope at 30 deg. as in Fig. 6. It can then conveniently be constructed about the true length diagonal with the aid of a 30 deg. set square, thus eliminating the projection of the minor diagonal. If the cube is completed, as has been done in Fig. 6, the resulting outlines are, of course, the well-known Isometric cube. In this all edges are foreshortened to the same extent, which is determined by the projectional relationship between the 45 deg. lines of the true plan and the 30 deg. lines of the rhombus. This fact may be used to find the correct length of the cube edges in the pictorial view, and the practical method of doing this is shown in Fig. 7. The true length is laid off on a 45 deg. line and projected vertically on to a 30 deg. line to give the required foreshortening. As all the edges of the Isometric cube are the same length, this ratio of foreshortening—in future called the 45/30 scale—will apply to all sides *including the verticals*.

The auxiliary view used in Figs. 3, 4 and 5 may now be dispensed with entirely, and the method is reduced as follows.

First the basic square, A (Fig. 7) is constructed, and the major diagonal of the rhombus drawn directly

FIG 7

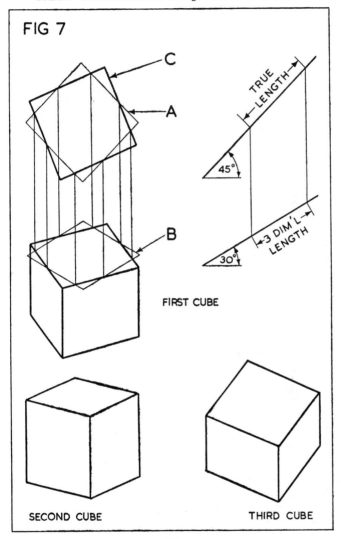

C

A

TRUE LENGTH

45°

B

30°

3 DIM'L LENGTH

FIRST CUBE

SECOND CUBE

THIRD CUBE

below. The standard rhombus, B, is then completed with a 30 deg. set square. The plan square C in the required rotational position is superimposed upon the basic square A, and projected to the rhombus to produce the required three dimensional outline. The pictorial cube is completed by marking off the foreshortened height, found by the 45/30 scale, along projectors dropped from the corners of the top face. This is very much quicker than the two-stage method, and its full worth will be seen when more complicated shapes are considered.

The reader may have noticed that in drawing the cube in Fig. 7 (and the Isometric cube) it is really unnecessary to use the 45/30 scale to find the apparent depth, as this length is given by that of the standard rhombus sides. The use of this ratio scale has been shown here, however, because it will later be instrumental as the basis for finding the depths of non-cubic solids.

As was stated earlier, the standardisation of the tilt angle is not the degree of limitation that it seems. In Fig. 7 two further outlines are shown, making three cubes in what appear to be entirely different positions. Actually they are one and the same view turned over to appear standing on different bases. The top of the first cube is the side of the second and the front of the third. Therefore, to project a view such as the second one, where the angle of tilt is slight, it is only necessary to project as already explained, and then turn the finished view round. An example of this technique applied to a more complex object will be seen in the next chapter.

Although the cube cannot be projected in absolutely

any position, the number it may be viewed in is still so very great that standardisation of tilt is amply justified.

So far a cube has been used to demonstrate the method. When it comes to real engineering components these are, of course, more complex in form. In the following chapters the Walters system is developed to cover the more practical shapes actually encountered in industry.

I V

THE great majority of engineering components take the form of geometrical solids, and are basically prisms with flat faces or turned solids of revolution, while a large number are combinations of the two. The cube, around which the method has until now been built, *is* a prism and, therefore, the step between this special one to prisms of more varied shape is not a great one.

If the square faces of the cube are changed to rectangular ones, the resulting solid is a rectangular prism, shown in Fig. 8. This may be drawn three dimensionally with only small modifications to the technique used for the cube.

In Fig. 8 the plan rectangle is placed in the required rotational position and the basic square drawn over it. It will be noticed that the relative positions are quite arbitrary, that is, the basic square is not symmetrically disposed about the rectangle as it was in the plans of the previous examples. It is not essential that it should be specially arranged, because corresponding points on the square and rhombus will always lie projectionally in line no matter where the points of intersection occur. These intersection points are, as before, projected from the basic square to the standard rhombus and the three dimensional view of the rectangular face completed by joining up the points so found.

The two points marked *A* used for projecting the

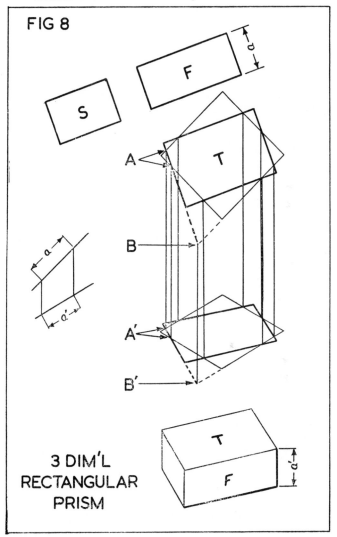

FIG 8

S

F

a

A

T

B

a

a′

A′

B′

T

F

a′

3 DIM'L
RECTANGULAR
PRISM

left edge fall so close together that a slight inaccuracy in the projection of either point would have a considerable effect on the slope of the required line in the three dimensional view. It is in general much better to have a fair distance between any two points on the same line in order to reduce this danger of inaccuracy. When they do fall close together, it is advisable to plot another point at some distance. This can be done by producing the line in question to meet an appropriate side of the basic square—or its continuation. Referring to point *B*, in Fig. 8, it is plain how this point has been projected on to the appropriate side of the rhombus produced to obtain a check on the slope of the three dimensional line. This method of producing lines should always be borne in mind ; it is not only a method of checking the slope of a line but it is often the only method by which the slope of some lines can be obtained. (See Fig. 31.)

The height of the prism must now be obtained. The angle of tilt is the same as that of the previous three dimensional cubes, so that the ratio of foreshortening is therefore the same. The true dimension *a* is transferred from the orthographic elevations to the 45 deg. line drawn aside from the main work. Projecting *a* from the 45 deg. line on to the 30 deg. line below, the foreshortened height *a'* is found. Dimension *a'* is stepped off on the verticals dropped from the corners of the pictorial top face and the view is finally completed as previously shown.

Fig. 9 explains how the three dimensional view of a triangular pyramid is projected. The orthographic drawing is pinned to the drawing board at the required angle of rotation. The base triangle is projected

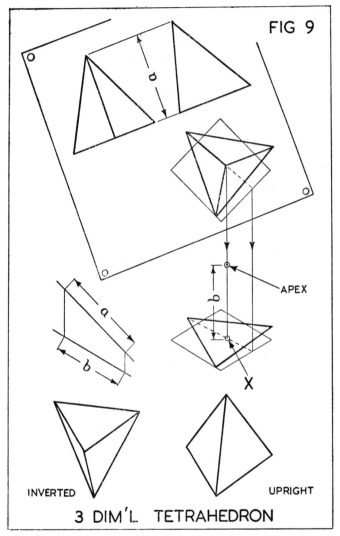

FIG 9

APEX

X

INVERTED   UPRIGHT

3 DIM'L TETRAHEDRON

from the points of intersection formed when the basic square is superimposed upon it. The manner is similar to that used in the previous examples but for clarity the projection lines to the rhombus are not shown. In any case, in practice, these lines are rarely needed, as it is sufficient to locate the required points by means of small ticks. As the required view is that of a pyramid and not of a prism, there is only one more point to be found. This point is, of course, the apex.

Fig. 9 shows clearly how the point above which the apex lies may be readily determined in the base. The true height, a of the apex is also easily taken from the front elevation and foreshortened by way of the 45/30 scale to length b, which is stepped off vertically from the point X found in the base. Naturally it is stepped off above point X and not below, as in the earlier examples. The possibility of stepping off b below X does exist, when the final view would be *inverted* as illustrated.

Having found the apex point, it only remains to join it to the three corners of the base triangle and the pictorial view is complete.

The further example in Fig. 10 is of an irregular pyramid cut so as to form an oblique top face. First the basic square is drawn. There is no limit to the size or position of the basic square, and in this case it is drawn large, all the edges in the plan being produced to meet the sides of the square in twelve points—six for each triangle. These points are projected on to the rhombus and joined up appropriately, resulting in the *final* outline of the base triangle, but only in the *plan* outline of the oblique top face. (Fig. 10(A).) It is, therefore, necessary to find the apparent

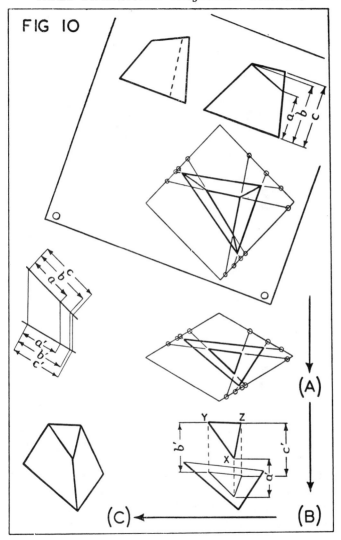

FIG 10

(A)

(B)

(C)

heights of the top face corners above the three dimensional *plan* outlines.

The true heights *a*, *b* and *c* are taken from the orthographic elevations, foreshortened by the 45/30 scale, and transferred as *a'*, *b'* and *c'* to their respective vertical projectors, which is clearly shown in Fig. 10 (B). The three points X, Y and Z, thus found form the corners of the triangle which is the correct view of the oblique top face at the chosen angle of rotation and at standard tilt. Joining the corners of this triangle to those of the base completes the view. (Fig. 10 (c).)

Although the last examples are based on the triangle, the same technique of producing outlines to meet the basic square may be used for the projection of any solid bounded by flat faces, irrespective of their number or slope. To illustrate this technique with a practical example, a pictorial view of a lathe tool is built up in Fig. 11 from the original drawings. It is not suggested that lathe tools need be shown three dimensionally, but they constitute good examples of solids with irregular sloping faces.

As can be seen in Fig. 11, the plan is rotated to what is considered a suitable position, and the three dimensional " plan " outlines are projected through the basic square and rhombus in a similar manner to that of the last example. (First stage.) The actual projection lines are again omitted for clearness. Stage 1 contains the "plan" three dimensional positions of all the corner points. Each one is finally found by stepping off its apparent height from its true height foreshortened through the 45/30 scale. Only one point is traced through in Fig. 11, but the others are, of course, found by applying the same technique.

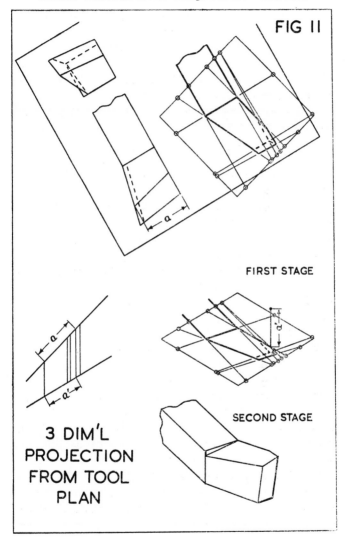

FIG 11

FIRST STAGE

SECOND STAGE

3 DIM'L
PROJECTION
FROM TOOL
PLAN

When all the corner points are located they are then appropriately connected and the result is an almost life-like view of the tool—second stage. Compare the outstandingly clear shape description of the three dimensional with the obscure outlines of the orthographic outlines.

So far only the plan views have been used as a basis for three dimensional projection. It will be remembered from Chapter III (Fig. 7) that many more varied views could be obtained by turning the cube round, and this technique can be used to great advantage on other solids.

The same lathe tool is shown projected in Fig. 12, but the basic square is drawn over an *elevation* instead of the plan. The method follows the same general pattern of the last example and may easily be followed through by studying the diagram. The orthographic elevation is treated as though it were a plan, while the heights are now taken from the true plan which serves in the capacity of a side elevation.

The second stage shows the completed three dimensional view *turned round* to stand on its proper base, and it will be noticed that the apparent angle of tilt is completely changed. A further, even more different view could be obtained by projecting from the other elevation, and as for each case the elevation used may be in *any rotational position* a vista of practically unlimited scope is opened for presenting different aspects of a component.

Orthographic projection as a means of shape description is used in industry over a very wide range of subjects. Space does not permit an extensive review of the various types of items which may be projected

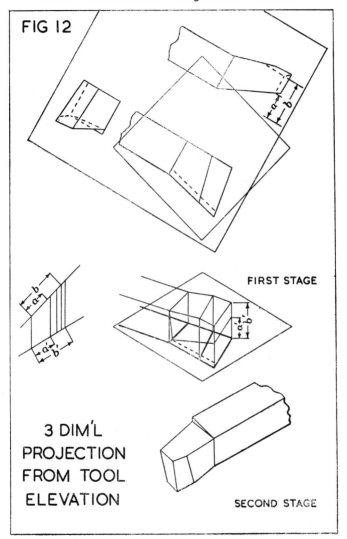

FIG 12

FIRST STAGE

3 DIM'L
PROJECTION
FROM TOOL
ELEVATION

SECOND STAGE

three dimensionally with advantage, but furniture, structural work, machine components, jigs, pipe runs, and a host of others readily lend themselves to this kind of treatment.

As an example, a *column base* has been projected three dimensionally in Fig. 13. The full construction is not shown, but, of course, it follows the usual pattern. After the base plan has been projected through the basic square and rhombus, the foreshortened heights of the gussets, base angles and base cleats are added. The reader will notice that only *two* heights have to be taken through this foreshortening stage.

The projection of this column base is, in fact, so simple that the time expended on it is less than that used in producing the orthographic plan. This sounds surprising, but the reason is obvious. In the three dimensional construction no measurement need be made, the whole procedure being entirely mechanical.

To be of use, the three dimensional view should be traced on to the same sheet as contains the ortho-graphic views, the views being complementary to one another. The tracing is usually best carried out by merely pricking through the corner points.

This three dimensional view gives instantaneously a clear picture of the finished job, and it is then simple to pick out the individual parts on the ortho-graphic drawings to ascertain dimensions and true shape.

For interest an *isometric* view of the same column base is shown below, where it can be seen that the base cleat is almost entirely hidden. As the base is symmetrical, it is impossible to make any other view

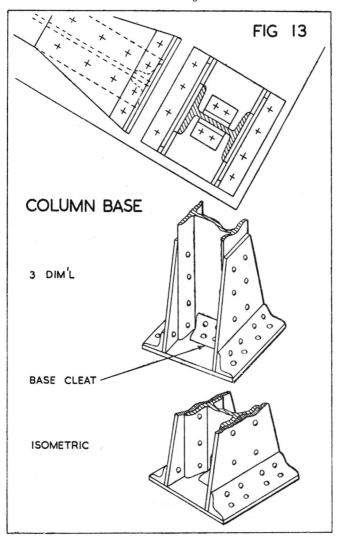

FIG 13

COLUMN BASE

3 DIM'L

BASE CLEAT

ISOMETRIC

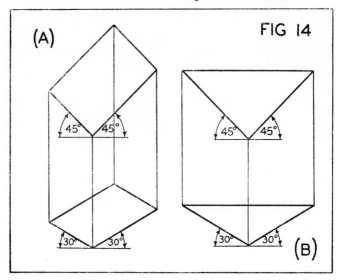

(except by reversing left to right), so that this base cleat will always be out of sight.

Most objects appear more natural in positions which do not border on the isometric position, but if a pure isometric view is desired, this may be obtained by the same methods with the plan rotated through 45 deg. In this case, with an object such as that in Fig. 13, there is no need to superimpose a basic square, as the base outlines themselves may be used for this purpose. The base may, of course, be rectangular instead of square, but this makes no difference.

Fig. 14(A) shows how a *rectangle* in the basic rotational position may be produced three dimensionally just as easily as the basic square's rhombus.

This modification is sometimes useful in normal

three dimensional practice. If an item to be projected is very long in comparison with its breadth, and it is impracticable to superimpose a basic square large enough for the purpose, a suitable rectangle may be drawn instead, the results being identical.

Similarly, at times, it is convenient to use only half of the basic square, that is a triangle, as shown in Fig. 14 (B). Later it will be seen that when an item consists largely of a circle, the circle itself and its three dimensional counterpart may be used for projection purposes.

In short, for three dimensional translation, *any* shape may be used as a basis, provided it can readily be represented three dimensionally at the standard tilt angle. These variations in no way supersede the technique of using the basic square and rhombus, as, in general, the latter are more suitable.

V

IN engineering there are only two solids of revolution which are of any importance. One, the cylinder, is most frequently encountered in the form of pipes, shafts, wheels and holes, while the other, the full or truncated cone, is found amongst other things in bevel wheels, taper shanks, and conical clutches.

These are, of course, based on the circle, and it is common knowledge that a circle assumes an elliptical shape when turned about any axis. In three dimensional presentation all circles are turned about one axis or another, so that the ellipse is of major importance to the draughtsman.

Ellipses may be drawn in the old fashioned way by plotting points—in fact, far too many students are still taught to do this, as if it were the only way—but the method is tedious and only theoretically accurate. Most draughtsmen use mechanical constructions for producing ellipses, which usually consist of approximating the true ellipse perimeter by dividing it into four circular arcs, as shown in Fig. 15. There are many different geometrical constructions for finding the four required arc centres, each varying in simplicity and accuracy. Perhaps the best, and the one generally used hereafter, is the " tangency method," illustrated in Fig. 16.

The major and minor axes, MM′ and NN′, are drawn (Fig. 16 (A)) and M joined to N to form the hypotenuse of the triangle MNK. The semi-major axis is swung about centre K to give point P on the minor axis produced. PN, the difference between the semi-major and semi-minor axes, is in turn swung on to the hypotenuse about centre N to give point L. The remainder of the hypotenuse, ML, is perpendicularly bisected, and the bisector produced to cut the ellipse axes (or axes produced) in two points, shown ringed. These are two of the required arc centres; the other two are marked off symmetrically opposite, as shown in Fig. 16(B). When these four centres are joined they form an XX pattern as can be seen. The required compass arcs merge smoothly at the points of common tangency, marked with arrow heads.

To draw the three dimensional view of a circle by the tangency method, it is necessary to know the position of the ellipse, the lines

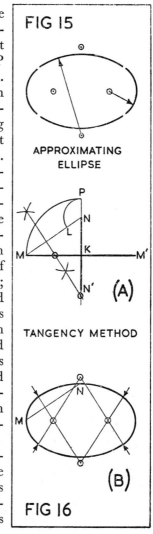

FIG 15

APPROXIMATING
ELLIPSE

TANGENCY METHOD

(A)

(B)

FIG 16

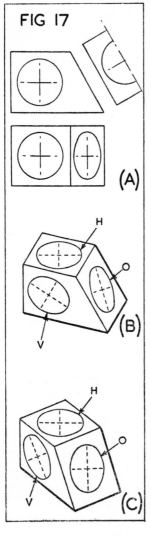

FIG 17

(A)

(B)

(C)

in which its axes lie, and the axes lengths.

An engineering component may contain circles which lie in horizontal, vertical or oblique planes, and all of these must be capable of being represented three dimensionally. Fig. 17(A) shows orthographically a block with circles on three faces—one horizontal, one vertical, and one oblique, while below in Fig. 17(B) and (C) the same block is illustrated pictorially in two different rotational positions. To construct the ellipses in these views their respective axes must be found (these are shown with broken lines). It can be seen that, as the block is rotated from the first to the second stage, the ellipses V and O change considerably in *shape* ; furthermore, the *slopes* of their axes also alter, and there appears to be no immediately apparent relation between these two variables and the rotation angle.

Ellipse H in the horizontal

top face is, however, a different proposition ; it remains constant and appears the same in both views. All the information required to draw this ellipse (or any other ellipse representing a circle in a horizontal plane) is readily found and the solution is shown in Fig. 18.

As a square can be inscribed within a circle, the corresponding standard rhombus must be inscribed within the required ellipse. All is known. The position is projectionally beneath. The major axis is the major diagonal of the rhombus, and, therefore, horizontal. Its length is equal to the diameter of the original circle. The minor axis is, of course, the minor diagonal of the rhombus. The ellipse may be constructed on these axes by the tangency method (Fig. 16) and as the circle and square may be made *any* size the three dimensional view of *any* circle in this position may be drawn.

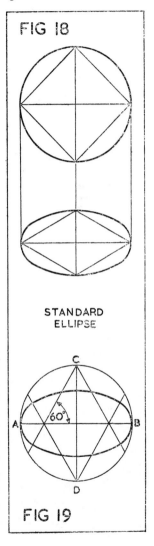

FIG 18

STANDARD ELLIPSE

FIG 19

35

There is, however, a more practical way of producing this *standard ellipse* as it is called. Comparing Figs. 16 and 18, it will be seen that the hypotenuse MN becomes one side of the standard thombus, so that at the standard angle of tilt MN lies at 30 deg. to the major axis. When this occurs, the XX pattern lines fall at exactly 60 deg. to the major axis, and it can be proved through similar triangles that the *lengths of the major and minor radii become respectively the sum and difference of the semi-major and semi-minor axes.*

In this favourable condition a special simplified construction for the standard ellipse is applicable. The true plan circle is described on the major axis (Fig. 19). The other diameter is constructed at right angles and the XX pattern lines are drawn through points C and D simply by using a 60 deg. set square. The points of intersection with the major axis give the centres for the minor arcs, which are struck with the appropriate radius. The major arcs are described about centres C and D using such a radius that the arcs meet smoothly on the 60 deg. lines. It is not necessary to find the minor axis as this is not used in the construction.

The treatment of non-standard ellipses such as V and O in Fig. 17, will be dealt with later, while the development of solids of revolution based on the standard ellipse is pursued in the next chapter.

VI

THE standard ellipse bears the same relation to the circle as the standard rhombus to the basic square ; That is, the standard ellipse and rhombus represent their respective plans tilted to the *same degree*. If the circle is given " thickness " it becomes a cylinder, and the apparent height in a three dimensional view may be obtained through the now familiar 45/30 scale.

In producing the pictorial view of a cylinder from the *orthographic outlines containing the circles* the standard ellipse representing the top face is first constructed (Fig. 20) by the method shown in Fig. 19. As the base of the cylinder is identical, the same ellipse is repeated below, the distance between the two major axes being the true height duly foreshortened through the 45/30 scale. The cylinder is completed by joining the two ellipses tangentially with two vertical lines.

It may be remembered that in building up the pictorial views in the previous chapters it was unnecessary to use two rhombuses in order to project the top and bottom faces of a component. In a similar way, it is not necessary to make two complete ellipse constructions. One ellipse must, of course, be constructed to find the arc centres and radii, but for the other ellipse the radii are the same, and the arc centres may be moved a length equal to the apparent height along vertical projectors through

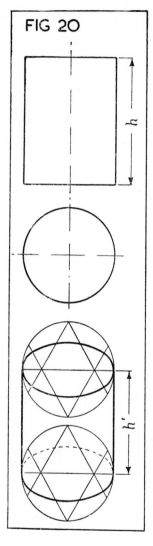

FIG 20

each one (Fig. 21). Similarly a vertical projector may be dropped from the points where the major and minor arcs merge to define their limits in the lower ellipse. The practical use of this is even more apparent when a greater number of identical ellipses have to be drawn, such as would be contained in, say, a three dimensional view of a number of thrust collars on a shaft. (This technique is used in Fig. 23.)

The pictorial representation of a right cone may be likened to that of the pyramid in Chapter IV, except that the base is an ellipse instead of a triangle. The process is so simple that no illustration is given. A standard ellipse is constructed within a circle whose dimensions are those of the true cone base. The apex lies immediately above the centre of the ellipse and its height is foreshortened from the true height by way of the 45/30 scale. The apex, when found, is joined tangentially to the base ellipse.

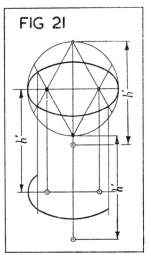

FIG 21

The full cone is very rarely met with amongst engineering solids, the most frequent form being the *truncated* cone. For drawing purposes, this is virtually half way between the cylinder and the full cone. Two standard ellipses are required, as in the cylinder construction, but they are of different size (Fig. 22), each being inscribed within circles of equivalent diameters to their counterparts in the plan. An inverted view may be obtained by transposing the ellipses as shown at the bottom of Fig. 22.

Most turned items are a combination of cones and cylinders, and as both may easily be drawn three dimensionally, almost any such complex item may be built up. The truncated cone of Fig. 22 has only to be placed on top of the cylinder of Fig. 20 and the result is a shaft with a taper on one end. Similarly, the inverted cone could be placed under the cylinder and the shaft would show tapers at both ends; or the smaller ellipse at the top of the truncated cone could be used as the base of another smaller cylinder. These are shown combined in Fig. 23(A). It is not necessary to draw each part separately, and Fig. 23(B) shows how they are all projected from the same plan. Working the other way about, any normal engineering

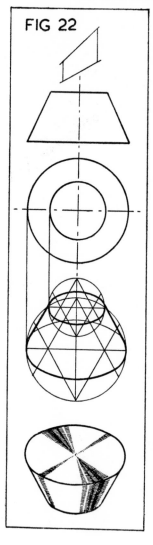

FIG 22

solid of revolution may be split up into cylinders and cones, and thence projected directly.

It will be noticed that in Fig. 22 the appearance of reality in the inverted view has been enhanced by the use of shading. This type of shading is used extensively in illustrative work for instruction and advertising, and is used to suggest a machined surface. Shading for use on production drawings is usually confined to the depiction of roundness alone, the degree of finish being contained in the specifications. The conventional method of drawing office shading for three dimensional views of turned solids is shown in Fig. 23, and consists of straight ruled lines becoming progressively closer and heavier towards the sides. Those lines on cylindrical surfaces are parallel with the axis, while those on cones or parts of cones, are radially disposed about the apex, which is found

FIG 23

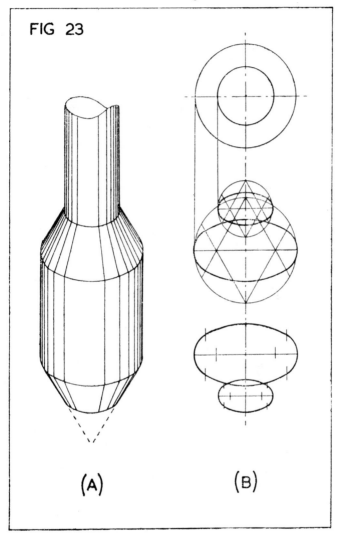

(A)   (B)

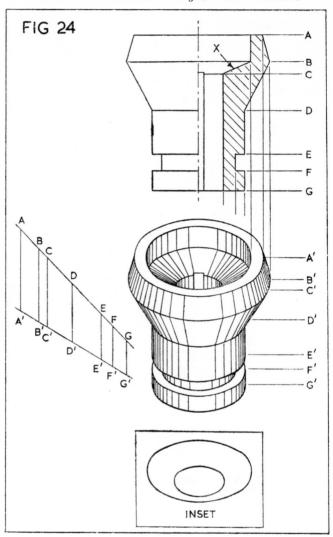

FIG 24

INSET

42

readily by producing the two sloping edges (see bottom of Fig. 23(A)).

Shading is not always necessary and should not be overdone. Examples will be found throughout this work of both shaded and unshaded drawings. There are times, however, when shading can be an integral factor in shape description, and such a case is shown in the following example (Fig. 24) representing part of a friction clutch.

It is built up entirely of cylinders and cones. The lines through the planes containing the circles, A, B, C, etc., are reproduced below as A', B', C', etc., the distance between each being scaled down by the standard ratio. The major axis of each ellipse is projected from the elevation and a standard ellipse constructed on each one. The cones and cylinders are then completed as necessary. Although the major axes lengths are taken from the elevation, the three dimensional view is still theoretically projected from the plan containing the circles, which has been omitted in Fig. 24.

This component contains an " internal " cone, marked X in the orthographic view ; in the three dimensional, this sloping surface would not be obvious unless shaded. For one thing, only part of each of its ellipses is visible, and even if both were in full view as illustrated in the inset, they could equally well represent two non-concentric circles in the same plane. The other surfaces are shaded to preserve uniformity of style as well as to intensify the solidity.

43

VII

HAVING dealt with the presentation of circles in horizontal planes, which three dimensionally appear as standard shape ellipses there remains the problem of depicting those which lie in vertical or oblique planes. These are shown in Fig. 25(A) (see also Fig. 17(B)).

The same object is reproduced in outline in Fig. 25(B), but with the ellipse on the vertical face considered as one end face of a cylinder. In this way many of the seemingly insoluable factors governing the construction immediately resolve themselves. As with the cylinders and cones drawn with the standard ellipse in the last chapter, the *minor axis of the ellipse lies in the line of the cylinder axis*, with the major axis, of course, at right angles to it. This is a fairly obvious fact, and may easily be verified by actual observation of cylinders. However, for those readers who may query this fact, two further " cylinders " are drawn below in Fig. 25(C) and (D) with the minor axes of their ellipses *not* lying in the line of the " cylinder " axes. These are obviously not cylinders ; they appear to be " squashed," that is to have elliptical rather than circular normal cross-sections.

When a circle is rotated about *any* diameter, it appears as an ellipse whose major axis is the diameter lying in the axis of rotation, that is, the major axis remains true length. The ellipse in Fig. 25(B) is the equivalent of a circle rotated about the major axis, so that *the major axis is true length*.

The first steps in projecting the three dimensional view of a circle in a vertical plane are, then, established. The plan and elevation of a cylinder similar to that of Fig. 25(B) is shown in Fig. 26(A). The cylinder axis XY is easily produced three dimensionally as X′ Y′ via the basic square and rhombus (not shown in the diagram for clarity), while the centre of the circle in plan view is projected on to X′ Y′ to give the centre of the ellipse. The major axis of the ellipse is drawn through this point at right angles to the axis X′ Y′ and the same length *d* as the true circle diameter. The minor axis lies in the same line as the cylinder axis, and the only unknown factor is its length.

If a square is fitted round the circle (Fig. 26(A)) it follows that the ellipse must

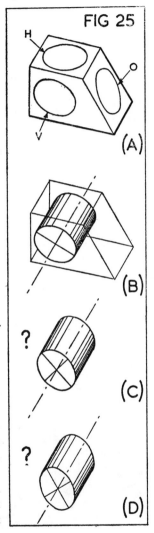

FIG 25

(A)

(B)

(C)

(D)

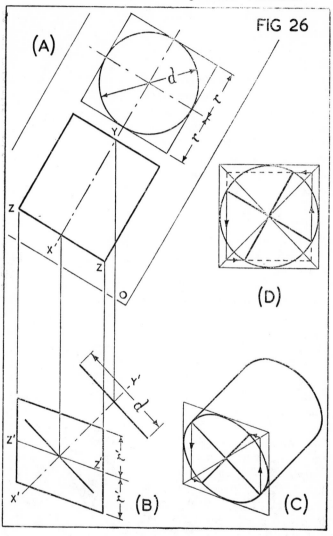

FIG 26

fit perfectly into the three dimensional view of this square (Fig. 26(c)). The latter is readily depicted and is, in fact, a surface similar to the front face of the cube in Fig. 6.

The horizontal diameter of the circle ZZ is first projected three dimensionally via the same basic square and rhombus as was used for projecting the cylinder axis. The three dimensional square is finished by shortening the height r, from the orthographic elevation, to r' via the 45/30 scale, and stepping it off vertically as shown in Fig. 26(B).

To find the minor axis, firstly one of the diagonals of this three dimensional " square " face is drawn (Fig. 26(c)). The extremities of the major axis are then projected parallel with the vertical sides of the crating square on to this diagonal, and thence parallel with the other sides to cut the cylinder axis, which is also the line of the minor axis. The end points of the minor axis are thus found, and the ellipse is constructed on the two axes by the tangency method illustrated in Fig. 16.

That this method of finding the minor axis, known as *projection by diagonals*, is correct is shown in two ways. Firstly, by the manner in which the ellipse fits perfectly into the square (there is a slight discrepancy in this fit when the minor axis is small in comparison with the major axis, which is due to the approximation of the ellipse perimeter) ; and secondly, by examining the orthographic view of this square face, which is shown in Fig. 26(D), it is clear that any one axis extremity projected by the diagonals embraces the other three axis extremities.

The full cylinder is virtually finished when the rear

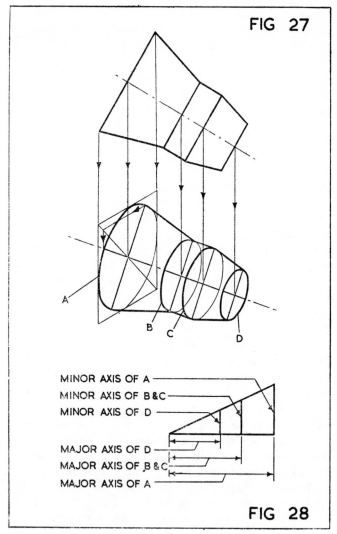

FIG 27

A

B

C

D

MINOR AXIS OF A
MINOR AXIS OF B & C
MINOR AXIS OF D

MAJOR AXIS OF D
MAJOR AXIS OF B & C
MAJOR AXIS OF A

FIG 28

ellipse is constructed. Its position is directly projected on to the cylinder axis, and, as the two ellipses are identical, the rear one may be reproduced in a similar way to that shown in Fig. 20(B), except that the projectors are parallel with the cylinder axis instead of vertical.

In practice the square need not be drawn round the circle in the elevation as it has been in Fig. 26(A). The height of the three dimensional square is foreshortened from the diameter of the circle, while its sloping sides are projected from Z-Z in the orthographic outlines which represents the circle's plan.

This technique may be developed to cover more complex solids of revolution just as the standard ellipse technique was enlarged upon. A simple item consisting of two truncated cones and a cylinder is shown projected three dimensionally in Fig. 27, from a view in which all the circles are in the vertical plane, that is they appear as straight lines in the plan.

It would obviously be a very complicated business if all the ellipses had to be constructed separately by the method just expounded. This is, however, not necessary. One ellipse, preferably the largest, is projected through all these stages. The other ellipses are all of the same proportion though of different sizes, so that the ratio between each pair of major and minor axes is constant. Where a number of ellipses have to be drawn representing circles on the same axis or in the same plane, it is convenient to draw a diagram similar to that in Fig. 28. It is in effect a graph, the slope of which is given by the found minor axis and the corresponding major axis. The minor axis of any other ellipse of similar shape is found by the use of

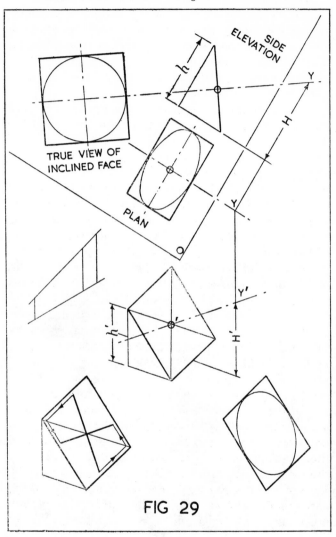

SIDE ELEVATION

TRUE VIEW OF INCLINED FACE

PLAN

FIG 29

its known major axis (true length) and similar triangles, as is clear in Fig. 28. The ellipse axes being found, each ellipse is mechanically constructed and all joined tangentially to show the correct shape.

There remains only the problem of the ellipse in an oblique plane (see Figs. 25(A) and 17(B)). Such a circle is illustrated in Fig. 29. The original drawings at the top consist of a plan and elevation together with an auxiliary elevation to show the true shape of the inclined surface. For convenience the circle is inscribed within a square face which is one surface of a wedge shaped prism. This would probably not be the case in practice, but it is easy enough to super-impose a square on to such a circle, and in most cases it is quite sufficient to imagine one there.

Essentially the problem is the same as the last one, that is the case of the vertical circle, and the solution is identical except that the axis through the circle OY (that is the axis of a co-axial cylinder) is not deter-mined three dimensionally quite so easily.

Referring to the three dimensional views of Fig. 29, the base of the prism is first projected through the basic square and rhombus (not shown); the height h is scaled down to h' and the three dimensional square face completed. The centre of the ellipse O' is deter-mined in this latter face by putting in the diagonals. To find the three dimensional counterpart of the axis OY it is necessary only to project one other point in it, such as Y which is marked in both plan and elevation. The method follows the normal pattern; the plan view of the axis is projected through the basic square and rhombus already drawn, and the height H above the base, foreshortened to H' is stepped off vertically to give point Y'. The three dimensional view of the axis OY is, therefore, O'Y'. This is all very clear in Fig. 29.

From here on, the procedure is identical with that followed for the vertical ellipse. The minor axis of the required ellipse lies along the axis O'Y', while the major axis is at right angles through O' and is the same length as the circle diameter. The length of the minor axis is found by projection via diagonals and the ellipse completed mechanically by the tangency method.

The development of this circle to solids of revolution follows the same lines as previously explained for the vertical circle.

It is strongly advisable to keep to the tangency ellipse throughout, even if the reader knows of more simple constructions, as this is one of the more accurate approximations. The reason why a close approximation is desirable will become apparent in the next chapter, where objects consisting of cylindrical *and* prismic shapes are built up.

VIII

THE majority of engineering components that call
for pictorial illustration are not simple shapes as have
been produced three dimensionally thus far, but even
the most complicated items may be "broken up"
into parts consisting of prisms and solids of revolution
—the latter usually being cylinders.

The item shown in Fig. 1 is such a combination of
basic shapes, and Figs. 30 and 31, show the stages in
building up a three dimensional view of this item.

As before, the original drawings are pinned to the
drawing board as in Fig. 30(A), with the outlines being
used for the projection in the desired rotational position.
With an object such as this, it is really quite arbitrary
as to which of the three outlines is called the plan,
but according to conventional orthographic layout,
the view used in this projection is the front elevation.

The basic square is superimposed upon the chosen
outlines. As this square may be of any size and in
any position, a little consideration in the choice of
these two factors can simplify the amount of work
entailed to some extent. In this case, one side of the
square has been drawn to pass through the centre of
the concentric circles at X, while another passes
through one corner at Y.

The standard rhombus is produced immediately
below in Fig. 30(B) and the centre X projected on to
it. The major arc about centre X is, for the moment,

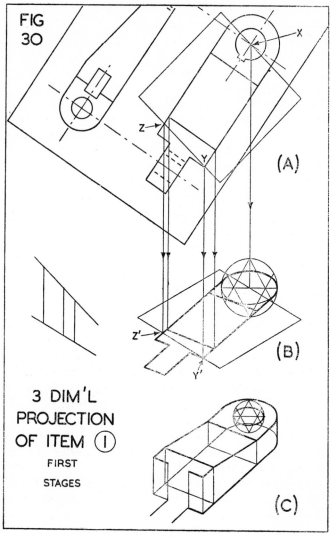

FIG 30

X

Z

Y

(A)

z'

Y'

(B)

3 DIM'L
PROJECTION
OF ITEM ①
FIRST
STAGES

(C)

considered as a full circle and is represented three dimensionally as a standard ellipse. Point Y is next projected on to the rhombus to give Y'. This point is joined tangentially to the ellipse. The opposite side may be drawn without any further projecting, as it is parallel with the side already drawn and is also tangential to the ellipse. The point Z has been projected in this case to serve as a check. The remainder of the three dimensional outlines are easily produced and need no further comment, except that no purpose is served at this stage by constructing the ellipse representing the smaller circle, that is the one containing the keyway.

Through the 45/30 scale the heights are added and joined up as in Fig. 30(c). The larger standard ellipse is repeated above at the required height by moving each of the arc centres up their vertical projectors (see Fig. 21). At this stage the smaller ellipse which is, of course, also of standard construction, is drawn.

The general appearance of the item is now becoming clear, the only important part yet to be shown is that which contains the other circles—that is those which appear in the true plan. The construction for these is that shown in the last chapter for circles which lie in a vertical plane. The larger circle is imagined crated in a square, which is shown in broken line in Fig. 31(D). This square is projected three dimensionally, the method being readily followed in the diagram. In practice the square need not be drawn round the orthographic circle, as it is sufficient to mark off the diameter of the full circle *d* on the face F. The reader will notice that there is a short cut in nearly

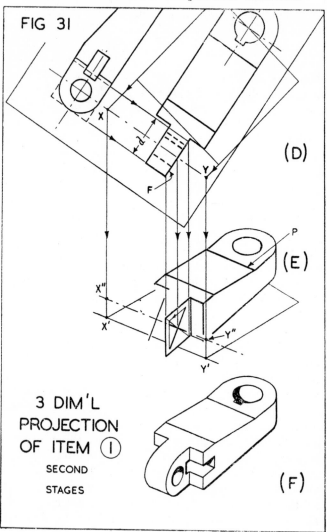

FIG 31

(D)

(E)

P

X''
X'

Y''
Y'

3 DIM'L
PROJECTION
OF ITEM ①
SECOND
STAGES

(F)

every stage ; these and many others are soon dis-
covered as the draughtsman becomes conversant with
this system of drawing. Using these short cuts the
method is not so long or so tedious as it might
appear.

The next step is to find three dimensionally the axis
of these circles, that is the axis XY in Fig. 31(D). The
general method is fairly clear in the diagram. Two
sides of the basic square are produced to meet the axis
in X and Y. These points are projected on to the sides
of the rhombus similarly produced (see Fig. 8) to give
points X' and Y', which are the " base " positions.
The height of the axis, foreshortened, is added to
give points X'' and Y''. The required axis lies
through these points.

The centre of the circle is directly projected on to
this axis; the major axis of the ellipse is drawn true
length through this centre and at right angles to
the axis X''Y'', while the minor axis is found by
projection via diagonals. The ellipse is completed
by the tangency construction; in this case only two
arcs are needed instead of four. The major axis of the
ellipse on the opposite face is produced and the corresponding arcs drawn.

In this particular projection, and in many others,
the three dimensional axis X''Y'' may be produced
by another short cut. The centre of the ellipse may
be projected on to the diagonal of the three dimensional square (see Fig. 30(E)). The required axis is
readily drawn through this point, as it is obviously
parallel with a number of other lines, amongst them
the one marked P.

The smaller ellipse on the face F is constructed on

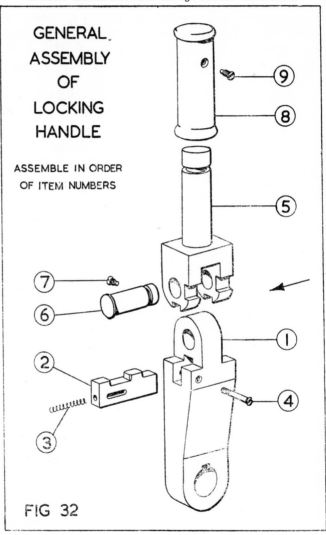

GENERAL
ASSEMBLY
OF
LOCKING
HANDLE

ASSEMBLE IN ORDER
OF ITEM NUMBERS

FIG 32

its axes, the major axis being true length, while the minor axis is found by similar triangles (see Fig. 28).

Very small ellipses which are not suitable for mechanical treatment should be drawn, either freehand or with french curves, about their true axes.

At this stage it is apparent that the rectangle shown in the orthographic plan can be nothing else but a slot; the vertical lines are directly projected, while the heights are found through the 45/30 scale. The keyway, shown in the three dimensional view in Fig. 31(F), also lies projectionally beneath its counterpart in the orthographic elevation.

Using the short cuts mentioned, the time taken in producing such a pictorial view is not so long as might be imagined; in this case it was not so long as the time spent on the orthographic outlines, simple as they are. It will be noticed that *never*, throughout the whole construction, was it necessary to measure any length or angle, the procedure being entirely mechanical.

Fig. 32 shows an exploded view of the complete assembly in which the item just drawn is a major part. The item—No. 1—is illustrated in this diagram in yet another position. It was, in fact, projected from the *plan* of Fig. 1. This can be appreciated by turning the drawing round until the standard shape ellipses appear to lie in a horizontal plane, i.e. when the drawing is viewed in the direction of the arrow.

Theoretically each item is projected separately and then traced on to a single sheet along the correct axes. This, again, seems a tedious and lengthy procedure, but in actual fact only Items Nos. 1 and 5 need be projected.

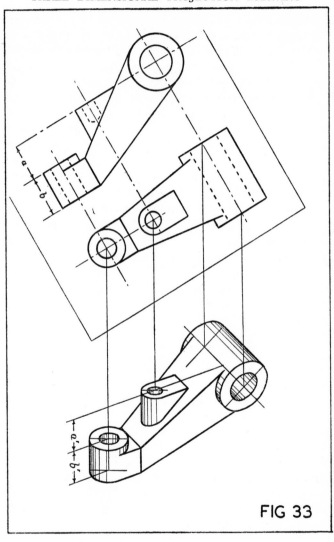

FIG 33

These two items must, of course, be projected from like orthographic views, which must be under the same angle of rotation. The one must be traced immediately above the other, although the distance between the items is quite arbitrary.

Now consider Item No. 6. It consists of standard ellipses on the same axis as that through the holes in Item No. 5, and the distance between the ellipses is obtained from the orthographic outline foreshortened through the 45/30 scale. In case it is not quite clear why *lengths* should be found by the 45/30 ratio, it must be remembered that during the actual drawing the whole picture is turned round and viewed in the direction of the arrow, when the " lengths " become heights.

Item No. 2 is produced similarly, its edges being continuations of the corners of the slot in Item No. 1, and the " lengths " found by the 45/30 scale.

The ellipses of Item No. 8 are all of the same proportion as those lying in similar planes in Item No. 5, but the " vertical " distances between them must be projected, as in the " drawing position " these lengths are horizontal.

Fig. 33 illustrates yet another simple item projected three dimensionally. Again the full construction is not shown, but the basic axes have been left in so that the reader may follow the general lines along which the component was built up. It consists, essentially, of two hollow cylinders connected with a tapering prism. The axes were first projected and the three dimensional cylinders constructed upon them. These were then appropriately joined up to form the rectilineal shape between them. The circles of the lug on top were then drawn and the lug completed.

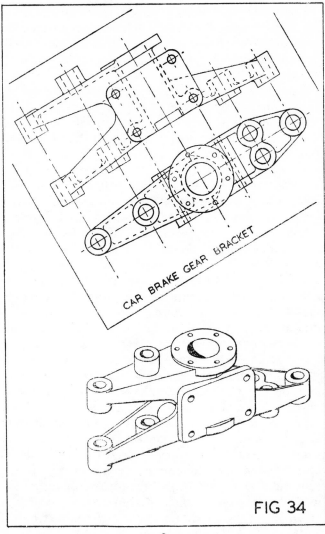

CAR BRAKE GEAR BRACKET

FIG 34

It will be noticed that there is a curve of intersection between the curved surface of this lug and the inclined surface it rests upon. As this curve is very small, it was estimated and drawn with french curves.

There are, however, many types of engineering drawings which contain large and complex curves of intersection. These need not be estimated, as they are capable of being projected in a manner similar to that employed for their orthographic determination. The scope of this book is not large enough to show the technique involved, especially as the method differs in detail with various types of curves.

The intelligent reader, who has grasped the principles thoroughly of three dimensional projection, will probably be able to work out of his own accord how the curve of intersection contained in the item of Fig. 33 could be projected. From there it is only a step to more complex curves.

However, those readers desirous of acquainting themselves with this section of three dimensional work will find many interesting examples in *Three Dimensional Engineering Drawing* by W. E. Walters, President I.E.D., F.I.E.D.

The last illustration, Fig. 34, is of an item chosen because of its similarity to that of Fig. 33, and projected straight from the orthographic outlines shown with no additional information. It is reproduced to allay the fears of those readers who still feel that three dimensional projection, interesting as it is, is impracticable when applied to the more complicated production drawings actually found in industry.

A very careful scrutiny of the diagram will show slight discrepancies comparing the orthographic with the three dimensional. This is to be expected, as during the drawing of the orthographic views, the draughtsman had to build up a mental picture of the complete component, and as was pointed out in the first chapter, this is not always reliable.

Three dimensional treatment does give an accurate, clear picture of a component, and any errors in the orthographic views will always show up. In this way, orthographic views are thoroughly checked, and any mistakes can be put right, thus ultimately saving expense and trouble.

To sum up, three dimensional drawing is simple and practicable. It serves firstly as a check to the draughtsman that his original drawings are correct, and secondly it presents a clear picture of what is required to the craftsman and to all those others concerned in the manufacture of an article. It does, in short, go a very long way towards cutting out errors all the way from a component's design to its ultimate manufacture.